95

EXPLOSIVE MUSCULAR POWER FOR

CHAMPIONSHIP
FOOTBALL

EXPLOSIVE MUSCULAR POWER FOR
CHAMPIONSHIP
FOOTBALL

JOHN JESSE
Foreword by John H. McKay
Head Football Coach — University of Southern California

THE ATHLETIC PRESS
P.O. Box 2314-D, Pasadena, California 91105

Acknowledgments

Sincere thanks are due the publisher, Donald Duke, who conceived the idea for this book and his encouragement, support and constructive suggestions.

I wish to express my deep appreciation and thanks to Bob Hoffman, Director of Athletics, Taft High School, a former football great at University of Southern California and Charles Bash, assistant football and track coach, Long Beach Polytechnic High School, for their review, suggestions and criticism of the subject matter.

A very special thanks to my son, Steve Jesse, a former college football player who posed for the exercise illustrations. He is an example of a young man who lacked the physical qualifications of size and physique, and through use of weight training developed the strength and body toughness required to successfully compete against much larger players without incurring injury.

Finally, I wish to thank the talented young man, Matthew Whittlesey, who prepared the equipment illustrations.

Foreword

In my opinion the gridiron is the last frontier for the development of good Americans. Young men succeeding in football are endowed with certain God-given talents. Those who achieve greatness are the individuals who constantly strive for improvement.

To achieve excellence one must be conscious of his physical and mental assets and be able to stimulate assets to maximum effort. *Explosive Muscular Power For Championship Football* provides a method by which young men can most effectively prepare to meet the rigorous demands of Championship Football.

JOHN H. McKAY
Head Football Coach
University of Southern California

Table Of Contents

The format is excellent and the material factual. It is outstanding in respect to the importance of strength development in the lower back and sides. The author has emphasized the importance of out-of-season conditioning. He places great emphasis on lifting form. In my opinion this is extremely important as most high school boys fall down in this regard.

ROBERT HOFFMAN
Director of Athletics
Taft High School
Taft, California

Without a doubt it is the best book and/or article that I have read on the subject. Most books are for the coaches and really don't reach the athlete at the high school level. This book does an outstanding job in that respect.

The author has placed a great deal of attention on the development of strength in the lower back and sides. The weight training program at Polytechnique High School has been doing this for the past four years at the author's suggestion and the result have been most rewarding.

The author has not overlooked the important factor of speed. It is my opinion that speed of movement is the most important aspect of any weight training program.

CHARLES E. BASH
Assistant Football and Track Coach
Long Beach Polytechnique High School
Long Beach, California.

Introduction

Football is the toughest team game in America and has become the nation's major high school and college participation sport. As fall semester bells ring, hundreds of thousands of young athletes with football shoes in hand rush to the gridiron with dreams of making the "Varsity." Many hopefuls make it tougher on themselves by going into the season "soft." Maximum performance demands peak conditioning. While many athletes possess the desire to play competitive football, they lack one or all of three essential requirements — strength, explosive power, or muscular bulk. This book is a new approach toward the improvement of these physical assets and capacity.

Most coaches tend to look for an athlete with size and strength, assuming that with size there will be comparable strength. A coach also hopes the young participant can be taught the basic football skills necessary to make the team. In high school especially, the athlete who meets the qualifications of size rarely possesses a level of strength and explosive power to move his body in a coordinated and powerful manner against an opponent who seldom remains in a set position. The coach tends to overlook the young man who possesses good coordination, but appears to be too small and/or weak to perform in good competition.

9

Strength, explosive power, and muscular bulk are three physical qualifications which can be developed and improved upon with 100 per cent success — if the potential football player is willing to spend an adequate amount of time and effort toward his development.

The writer has long maintained that strength development in one area of the body (lower back and sides) is generally overlooked in modern day weight training programs. Many athletes develop tremendous strength in the muscles of their arms, shoulders and legs, yet pay little attention to the lower back and sides. In turn, the athlete never develops a high level of total over-all body strength.

This book was designed for the individual who wishes to improve his physical qualifications for football. Great emphasis has been placed on strength development of the lower back and sides, regions which enable the athlete to explode with tremendous power in lateral and rotational body movements. These actions are common to the sport of football, but not to weight lifting from which modern day strength conditioning programs have evolved.

In order to make the "Varsity," the present day athlete MUST be capable of moving with explosive power in lateral and rotational movements with the same degree of power displayed in straight ahead or vertical movements. Strength, explosive power and muscular bulk can be developed and we will show you how!

JOHN JESSE — 1968

1

Pre-Season Conditioning

FOOTBALL CONDITIONING for high school and college players MUST be done out of season. The competitive period is far too short to permit a single coach or small physical education staff the required time to properly condition each player for the first game. In a couple of short weeks, the coach attempts to teach his team the intricate skills and techniques required for participation in the game. It takes a full semester to learn basic algebra or chemistry; certainly football conditioning requires a full season!

Trainers, coaches, and medical doctors associated with athletics recognize that every athlete, in order to perform his best during the football season, must remain in good physical condition throughout the year. The coach who must handle daily physical education or gym classes in addition to his football schedule does not have the time to program individual physical training tailored to each players needs.

Authorities concerned with athletic injuries are of the opinion that "Crash Program Training" of the American athlete is the principal cause of needless bench warming resulting from injuries. Athletes, particularily in a one season sport such as football, tend to reach their highest level of performance half-way through the season. It should be noted that most of the serious and fatal accidents and injuries occur at

11

the beginning of the season. Many of these injuries are due to the lack of proper and adequate pre-season physical conditioning.

This national problem was expounded at the recent National Athletic Trainer's Association convention where they adopted a resolution aimed at protecting high school and college football players from injury. The measure called for, "The first five days of pre-season football practice to be devoted entirely to physical conditioning." While this is a step in the right direction, it is obvious that several months of moderate training is far superior to a five day crash program. So far, there has been no short cut method devised that will adequately condition an athlete for participation in any type of bodily contact sport. Year-around football conditioning is the only answer to strength development and muscular bulk for injury prevention.

2

Physical Requirements

The young athlete who has the desire and is willing to pay the price to play football must possess or develop certain physical qualities if he expects to make the team and play regularly. The combination of strength, explosive power, agility (movement) and stamina are prerequisites for participation in football and every form of athletics. The outstanding characteristics of the most successful athletes in team sports are explosive power and agility.

Here are seven physical qualities required for high school and college football:

1. AGILITY (Movement) — Football requires that an athlete outdo his opponent physically while in movement. This means that above all he must develop the ability to *move quickly in any direction* with his body under control at all times. Agility includes the factors of explosive muscular power, quickness, balance (a solid position at the point of contact with the opponent), flexibility and timing. The athlete who does not move well is likely to have great difficulty in learning the basic skills of football.

2. FLEXIBILITY — The range of motion through which body parts can move is an important part of the quality

13

of movement; the ability to twist, bend, and reach in playing defense or in attaining a low well-balanced position for offensive blocking is dependent on the degree of flexibility an athlete possesses.

3. SPEED — Speed is necessary in football, but the type of acceleration we speak about is not that of a sprinter in a 100 yard dash, but quickness — a fast explosive start or a speedy sideways movement in a specific area.

4. SIZE — Size is an asset only in high school and college football. Quickness and speed counterbalance size, particularly in high school football. Many young men are large for their age and attracted to the game of football because they appear to have the physical requirements for a football player. Many lack quickness, speed, maneuverability, agility and balance, and are easily outmaneuvered and physically overcome by athletes of small stature.

5. STRENGTH — Where one athlete competes against another in team sport, the stronger of the two possesses the distinct advantage. Which has the better chance of handling a 210 pound opponent — an athlete with the leg strength to lift 210 pounds or the man with the strength to lift 350 pounds? The answer is obvious. Among athletes having similar abilities in agility, coordination and application of football skills, a good strong athlete will always win over the weaker opponent. Strength also assists in making up for lack of size.

6. EXPLOSIVE POWER (Strength in Action) — A product of force times velocity (speed). In sports, force is generally or entirely derived from muscular strength. Jim Taylor, the Green Bay Packers fullback, is an example of a player with great explosive power. Weighing approximately 215 pounds, yet he is capable of knocking over a 250-270 pound defensive lineman.

7. STAMINA (Endurance) — There are two types of endurance — muscular and circulo-respiratory (heart and

14

lungs). Muscular endurance is greatly dependent on the strength level of the individual and his circulo-respiratory efficiency. The primary factor in all sustained endurance activities is the amount of oxygen supplied the muscle by the blood stream and this is dependent on circulo-respiratory efficiency. The greater this efficiency, the greater the oxygen supply to the muscles during muscular effort. There is no substitute for running as a method of developing circulo-respiratory endurance. For this reason, running is highly stressed by all football coaches and trainers as a very important part of a player's physical conditioning.

One important thing to remember is that — all seven qualities can be developed or improved upon. Yes, even size. A weak 5-foot 7-inch, 140-pound athlete can develop himself into a strong, powerful and quick 5-foot 7-inch, 170-pound athlete. A 6-foot 3-inch, 250-pound athlete can trim himself into 220 pounds of solid muscle possessing great explosive power and agility. It can be done if each player is willing to sacrifice, work hard, and follow the programs set forth in this book.

3

Football Weight Training Objectives

The young athlete who takes up weight training, has a tendency to direct his training toward strength development and large muscular size rather than strengthen himself for athletics. He develops the type of strength required for lifting heavy weights from the floor, or the type of muscles which look nice while posing in front of a mirror. In his training sessions he uses extremely heavy weights requiring very slow movements to the exclusion of all other types of exercise with or without weights. He will gain strength and/or size but will become slow and cumbersome on the gridiron.

The basic objective in a football weight training program is to develop an *overall total body strength* that will enable the athlete to express *explosive muscular power in movement.*

The high school and college football athlete requires tremendously strong legs in order to apply the skills of blocking and tackling — to provide the drive and power necessary to move a heavy opponent. He needs strong arms and shoulders to make himself more effective in manipulating his upper body during blocking and tackling. Today, more than ever, due to the type of blocking and tackling used in football, it is mandatory the player develop an extremely strong neck.

Generally overlooked in football weight training programs is the great importance of tremendous strength in the mid-section and lower back. Football is one of the few sports where participants use the entire body, many times at great speed, in purposeful body contact against an opponent. In making his moves, the player is generally not in a fixed position when exerting his strength. In numerous cases, particularly on defense, this involves lateral movement, many times of a violent *rotational* nature, as compared to the straight ahead movement of the sprinter, or the vertical (upward) movement of the weightlifter.

The football player may have great strength in his arms, shoulders and legs, but will not be able to make the most effective use of his strength in other areas of the body unless he develops comparable strength in his mid-section and lower back. Mid-body strength ties in the solidity of the extremities and provides a greater over-all body force in athletic movements.

The second objective is to develop strength in the muscles and ligaments surrounding body joints particularly vulnerable to injury during practice or in a game situation. Injury statistics disclose the knee, ankle, shoulder, and neck are the most vulnerable joints. Great athletic ability, strength, or large size will not help the team or coach if the athlete is sitting on the bench for an entire season with an injured knee.

4

Combating Football Fatigue

Throughout this book we emphasize the development of explosive force for football players. This force must be displayed in an all-out effort during the entire game or practice session — not for only a couple of minutes. How can a player develop this ability?

We mentioned previously that circulo-respiratory endurance was a physical requirement for football participation. One aspect of this quality is the ability of the individual to tolerate an oxygen debt. What is oxygen debt? In the performance of any physical activity, the body requires a certain amount of oxygen. In moderate activities such as slow running, light calisthenics, paddleboard, golf, etc., the circulo-respiratory system provides enough oxygen to meet the demands of the activity. In other activities like fast running, the body cannot meet the oxygen requirements for the activity and an oxygen debt is created. This is manifested by a state of breathlessness displayed by the athlete after the activity is completed. This debt must be repaid during the rest interval between violent or high intensity effort.

Being capable to cope with oxygen debt requires physiological (organism's healthy functioning) adaptations of the body. Just as important is the psychological (acting through the mind) tolerance of the stress, pain, torture and agony

18

associated with physical effort while short of breath. Football coaches recognize this problem and will condition their players to the physiological adaptations of the body and the psychological tolerance of high oxygen debt through wind sprints done after practice when the player is already fatigued. One important factor is overlooked in wind sprint training. This activity involves running at high speed for a short distance, but without any consideration of the resistance factor encountered by the players in performing football skills.

A football game or practice session requires 100 to 150 all-out efforts against resistance covering a time period between five to 15 seconds for each effort interspersed with a 20 to 25 seconds rest interval. These all-out efforts against resistance require a great expenditure of energy and the body therefore has a need for a much greater supply of oxygen to meet its requirements than needed for running alone. The rest intervals generally are not without some type of activity by most of the team members, such as down field blockers, pass receivers, and the ball carrier and blockers returning to the huddle.

It can be easily seen that a player is engaged in a series of oxygen debt bouts and incomplete rest periods. This results in a gradual increase in general body fatigue which in turn affects the players skill and explosive effort toward the end of the game. The factor we feel that is overlooked in conditioning for football is the psychological aspects of an all-out effort against resistance when the body has become fatigued.

It is well established that the limit of an athletes strength expression is largely dependent upon the degree of inhibition which acts to limit an all-out maximum effort. Behind this inhibition lies many causes, but one of the most important in athletic competition is the unwillingness of the individual to endure the discomfort (stress, pain, torture and agony) of an all out attempt, particularly when he thinks or feels he is tired or his team is behind in the game.

To offset and counteract this inhibition, the athlete must be psychologically conditioned to put forth a maximum effort

19

when tired. This cannot be accomplished by running wind sprints alone, but can be overcome through a specific type of weight training program while at the same time the football player is developing strength, muscular endurance, explosive power and dynamic agility.

5

Strength Development Methods

When we analyze the physical qualities required by the young athlete who participates in football, we can easily recognize that the physical quality common to all is muscular strength. It is the easiest to develop of all physical characteristics required for athletic performance.

What is the most effective method for the development of strength in an athlete who has the desire to play football or wishes to improve his performance on the practice or playing field? The use of dynamic tension, isometric contractions, calisthenics, gymnastics, chest expanders, pulley weights, attaching weights to the body, buddy type exercises, hill and mountain climbing, running in snow, sand or up the stadium steps, heavy labor, weight lifting, and weight training have all been advocated at one time or another as means of acquiring muscular strength. There is no question that all these methods will develop strength in the body or its component parts in varying degrees, but most of these methods possess one or more limitations in its use.

Of all these methods, weight training is the most effective method for the development of strength. Total energy output and time is minimal as compared to mountain or hill climbing, heavy gymnastics, heavy labor or running in snow or sand. Weather conditions do not prevent its use. Participation

21

is not limited due to a lack of gymnasium equipment, hills, sand dunes, or stadium steps. The loads lifted can be adjusted to individual capacity — the weakest individual can participate. Strength training can be done in the privacy of one's home. Adjustable weights provide a measure of strength development that assists in continuous motivation. The two most important advantages are: (1) the "overload" principle can be made progressive by a gradual increase in weights used, thereby assuring a continuity of strength gains in desired body areas, and (2) weight training can be used to develop strength in any or all muscles of the body according to their individual capacities and the requirements of the sport in which the athlete participates.

6

Weight Training Principles

Here are eight principles that must be followed if you are going to get the best results from your weight training sesssion.

1. The dominating principle in strength development is "overload." Muscles must be compelled to carry out work beyond that which can be performed comfortably, easily and without strain.

2. The second principle of strength development is "progression." The amount of weight (load) used in an exercise must be reset whenever the athlete becomes able to complete the number of required repetitions with less than all-out effort. The practical way to determine whether the athlete can adhere to the principles of overload and progression is to perform an exercise with a stated load and number of repetitions. If he does not strain to complete the last two or three repetitions, he will know immediately that he is using a weight which is not heavy enough to fulfill the "overload principle." This will require an increase in the weight that is used for the exercise.

3. Tension is the basic stimulus for strength development. The athlete must exert maximum tension throughout the entire range of motion if he expects to develop the strength of the entire muscle. This requires that a weight training move-

ment used for pure strength development should be done in a smooth and even manner and at a moderate rate of speed.

4. The principle of "specificity" applies in strength training. The "specificity" principle is based on: (a) the requirements (force, speed and duration) of the sport for which the athlete is training and (b) the requirements of the athlete himself. In meeting the requirements of the sport for which he is conditioning himself, the athlete will employ the factors of load (weight used), rate (speed of exercise) and duration (repetitions). Pure strength is developed by the use of maximum weights with few repetitions. Muscular endurance is developed by reducing the weight and performing more repetitions. Muscular growth is promoted by the use of near maximum weights with a moderate number of repetitions. To develop explosive power and dynamic agility, the weight should be reduced so the exercise can be performed at a much faster pace. The athlete must consider his physical strong points and deficiencies. In addition to strengthening the muscles used in football and developing strength in the muscles and ligaments surrounding body joints for the prevention of injury, does he require greater strength in his arms and shoulders, greater body bulk, a stronger neck, etc.?

5. To increase explosive power (strength in action) the athlete must progressively increase the load at regular intervals.

6. Every total body movement, such as required in football, brings into play the prime mover muscles required to perform a specific skill movement and also the antagonistic muscles and the fixation muscles which stabilize and support other parts of the body during the specific movement. This is the primary reason why, when training with weights for a particular sport, the athlete should attempt to exercise the entire body as one unit. The exception to this principle would be in the development of strength in localized areas of the body.

7. The athlete should utilize a full normal range of motion while performing each strength development exercise. This means complete flexion and extension of the muscle. A

complete stretch of the muscle through a full range of movement develops strength in all areas of the muscle and eliminates the possibility of any permanent shortening of the muscle which could result from habitually performing an exercise over a limited range of motion.

8. An important point that should not be overlooked in a strength development program is the *will* to perform a physiologically maximum effort. Gains in strength development will only occur if the athlete is *willing to constantly put forth greater efforts* at regular intervals with the intention of exceeding his previous level of strength growth and accomplishment.

7

Injury Prevention

Football is a game of violent body contact which results in a high incident of injuries to the musculo-skeleto system. Most of the injuries sustained by the participant involve the lower extremities (ankles and knees); however shoulder injuries are rather common and during the past few years there has been an increased number of injuries sustained by the neck.

Most of these injuries are caused by excessive strains placed on the muscles and ligaments of the various joints which may give way with the rupture of the ligament(s) partial or complete.

One of the basic factors that contribute to a high injury potential in football is a lack of proper physical conditioning. A lack of strength in the muscles and ligaments surrounding body joints, a low level of muscular endurance, unbalanced muscular development, and lack of flexibility make an athlete highly susceptible to injury, particularly strains and sprains of the body joints already mentioned.

Trainers, coaches and physicians are unanimously agreed that vigorous physical conditioning and a high degree of athletic fitness is an absolute prerequisite to safe participation in sports and will assist in eliminating the most common type of injuries — strains and sprains.

The components of athletic fitness are strength, stamina and flexibility. A weight training course for football players should include specific exercises designed to increase these qualities in the muscles surrounding the ankles, knees, shoulders, and neck. Muscular bulk serves as a form of pad to cushion the impact of violent body contact. This is particularly true for the abdomen, lower ribs and kidneys. One-half inch of muscle added to the back of the neck is good protection in case the back of the helmet is forced down against the cervical spine.

Generally overlooked in books and courses on football conditioning is the fact that the ligaments themselves can be directly strengthened through progressive strain being placed on them. Dr. C. H. McCloy receives the credit for being the first person in the athletic world to stress the great importance on strengthening the ligaments, in addition to the muscles. He pointed out that ligaments of the knee, ankle and shoulders can be strengthened and increased in size when progressively greater stresses are systematically and directly applied to them. The ligaments, in addition to being strong, must be sufficiently pliable so that a certain amount of strain can be taken by stretch without rupture. This requirement can only be achieved by a properly directed and constantly practiced program.

In contrast to statistics published regarding the traditional type of football injuries, little has been said concerning injuries to the lower back and middle back — muscular strains and sprains. Strains of the lower back are less obvious to the human eye and the football player is not apt to report them to a coach or trainer. He will bear the inconvenience of a good night's sleep, or the strain may only be painful when he makes an all-out effort against resistance during a lateral or rotational movement of the entire body. Back strains can effect his reaction to the moves of an opposing player or cause him to reach with his arms to tackle instead of meeting a ball carrier head-on with his shoulder backed by a powerful body charge.

27

Thirty years ago a person rarely heard of an athlete suffering from low back strains. Most of the boys came from the farm, mines, mills, lumber camps, and waterfront docks, and as kids they worked with light loads — sledge hammers, axes, pick and shovel, etc. By the time they reached high school they were capable of lifting fairly heavy loads eight hours a day in many unnatural positions that involved movements of a rotational nature. Today the advice given to people in all walks of life is lift with the back straight. How many movements in football are done with a completely straight back against the resistance of an opponent who is not standing still in a set position similar to a weight or box on the floor?

The athlete will never develop strong, flexible and heavy back muscles by performing the traditional dead lifts and back hyperextensions recommended in weight lifting and weight training courses. He will have to start with light weights, performing round back lifts, and rotational trunk movements and gradually increase the weight used. In one year's time, he can have strong, well developed and flexible back muscles. The added bulk protects the kidneys and lower ribs. The increased strength and flexibility will practically insure the football player he will not be benched for the season due to a strained back.

8

Weight Training
For Special Skills

Two of the basic football skills are passing and kicking.
Muscular movements required in the performance of these
skills must be considered in selecting exercises that will
strengthen the muscles involved.

KICKING — In punting or place kicking, the player's legs fur-
nish the power for the force exerted against the ball. Hip
flexor strength is of great importance to the kicker in bringing the leg forward. As the leg is brought forward in a slightly
flexed position, the lower leg is forcefully extended by the
action of the quadriceps (front of the thigh) muscle.

PASSING — This movement involves a rotational movement
of the body. Power is generated by the side muscles of the
mid-section, the flexors of the shoulder (front of the shoulder
and upper chest muscles), the arm extensors (back of arm)
and the flexors of the wrists and hands. One of the most important muscle groups involved in the act of throwing are the
serratus anteriors, the little sawtoothed muscles that appear
to be between the ribs. They act in pulling the scapula (shoulder blades) forward and anatomically speaking, all movements of the shoulder strongly involves the scapula. Dr. Mc-
Cloy at the University of Iowa devised a specific exercise to
develop these muscles that are of great importance to passers,
javelin throwers and baseball players.

9

Nutrition And Weight Training

There are two vital facts which must be considered in connection with diet and athletics. (1) Although World or Olympic champions come from all types of cultures, racial backgrounds, nationalities, and living conditions, and their dietary patterns vary, there is one characteristic pattern common to all — sufficiency of food to meet energy requirements. (2) The nutritional requirements for an athlete in training are based on the identical fundamental principles that govern the nutritional needs of human beings in general — a balanced diet that furnishes sufficient calories, amino acids, vitamins and minerals needed for growth development and the daily activities of living.

Energy food intake values are determined by the number of calories a specific food contains. Calories tell how much energy is furnished the body. A young football player should eat a large amount of food sufficient to provide enough energy for all of the other activities he participates in each day and for normal growth and development. For normal everyday activities without participation in any form of athletics or weight training, a growing young man requires a food intake which supplies 15 calories per pound of body weight each day. During football season, a 200-pound player would need approximately 5,500 calories (3,000 for normal activity, 2,500 for football practice) each day to maintain his body weight.

Calories for energy production and growth are obtained from the three basic nutrients — proteins, carbohydrates and fats. The importance of protein requirements for the high school football player should be mentioned.

A high school football player using a weight training program to increase his strength and body size (bulk) should be guided by the following: (1) Daily intake of 130 to 150 grams of protein; (2) Protein should be eaten at all three meals each day; (3) The higher the intake of protein the greater is the need for an adequate intake of alkaline food and vegetables to counteract the increased load on the kidneys. He does not require expensive protein pills or powders to satisfy these requirements. Meat, fish, poultry, eggs, milk, cheese, dried peas and beans are the primary sources of protein. A quart of whole milk provides 35 grams of protein. A cheap way to increase protein intake is to add one package of skim milk powder, which can be obtained at any grocery store (5 packages for approximately 70 cents), to each quart of whole milk. The skim milk powder provides an additional 35 grams of protein.

A balanced diet according to nutritionists should include foods from the following groups: (1) Meat, poultry, fish, eggs, dried peas and beans; (2) Milk, ice cream, cheese; (3) Bread, cereal and flour; (4) Butter and fats; (5) Potatoes, vegetables and fruits; (6) Green and yellow leafy vegetables, citrus and raw cabbage.

WEIGHT GAIN — Adding 1,000 calories per day to the diet will increase the body weight about two pounds per week, if the athlete does not increase his daily activities. A growing athlete will expend about 3,500 calories per day in normal activities, gym classes, etc. Adding 300 calories of energy expenditures for a weight training session the athlete would require 5,000 calories per day to gain weight. In eating this amount of food, it is better to eat five or six times a day instead of three large meals. Eat smaller portions at meal time but supplement the meals with snacks at mid-morning, mid-afternoon and one hour before going to bed.

High calorie foods include ice cream, cream, butter, cheese, candy, jellies, jams, bread, pies, cake, beans, spaghetti, potatoes, pork, bacon, sausage, ham, sandwich spreads, gravies, etc. A liquid diet is the easiest way to gain weight. The digestive system can handle this type of increased food intake much easier than with the more bulky foods. A high calorie drink with a high protein content can be made by taking one quart of whole milk, adding three scoops of ice cream, two packages of skim milk powder, one banana, three tablespoons of peanut butter and mix them in a blender. This drink will provide approximately 100 grams of protein and 2,000 calories and if consumed during the snack periods is a good supplement to the regular three meals.

A football player who is attempting to gain weight with the aid of a weight training program should make every effort to refrain from other types of activity such as running, light calisthentics, etc., until he attains his desired weight level. The best time to engage in a program of this type is after football season and prior to spring practice or between the end of spring practice and one month after the beginning of summer vacation. A weight gaining program places a heavy strain on the digestive system and the kidneys and should not be engaged in for a period longer than eight weeks and by a young man under 16 years of age. At least eight hours and preferably nine hours of sleep should be obtained each night.

WEIGHT LOSS — The only way to lose weight is to reduce food intake or increase body activity. The best way is to do both at the same time. The overweight football player still requires strength, agility and endurance if he expects to make the team. He will use a weight training program to develop strength, and engage in agility exercises to improve his ability to move quickly, but will also concentrate heavily on endurance activities that burn up a large amount of calories. Reducing your food intake 500 calories per day and increasing your activities to burn up an additional 500 calories per day will result in a loss of one pound body weight every four and one-half days. You should increase the repetitions and use lighter weights during the weight training session supplemented each day by running or a similar activity. Avoid the high calorie foods already mentioned, concentrating on lean meats, fish, plenty of fruits and vegetables. Omit cake, pie, pastries, candy and other high carbohydrate (sugar and starch) foods. Eat only three meals each day and nothing between meals or before going to bed. It is best to eat a large breakfast and cut down the size of your evening meal. Sleep eight hours only and make every attempt to be more active each day. Walk or use a bicycle instead of riding in cars. Be more active in gym class, taking every opportunity to engage in sports that involve a large amount of body activity, especially running.

10

Weight Training Equipment

Basic equipment required for the programs outlined in this book consist of: (1) A barbell five to seven feet in length with collars for holding the weights in place; (2) Two dumbell handles, 12 to 16 inches in length with four collars; (3) An assortment of plates 1½, 2½, 5, 10, 15, 20 and 25 pounds. Including the bar, there should be sufficient weights to total 250 pounds; (4) Two iron boots, for use in performing exercises that develop the muscles surrounding the knee joints; (5) A bench ten to 12 inches wide, 18 to 24 inches high and three to four feet in length; (6) A head strap that can be used to support heavy weights in the squat and bench press exercises of the basic strengthening course if the athlete works out alone; (7) A chinning bar for use with the football muscular power program and for strengthening of shoulder ligaments.

A total investment of less than $100 will cover the cost of equipment cited above, although equipment such as the bench and squat stand can be constructed of wood. Construction of these two pieces of equipment are presented with list of materials required. The exercise bench and squat rack can be put together with simple household tools if the wood is pre-cut at the lumber yard.

SQUAT RACK

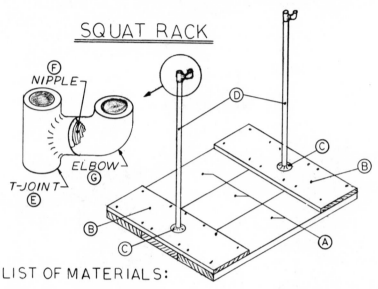

LIST OF MATERIALS:

- (A) 3 : 2"×12"×48"-LONG
- (B) 2 : 1"×12"×36"-LONG
- (C) 2 : 1½" PIPE FLANGES
- (D) " : " PIPING-48"LONG
- (E) " : " T-JOINTS
- (F) " : " NIPPLES
- (G) " : " ELBOWS

CONSTRUCTION DETAILS:
  ① USE OF SCREWS IS
     PREFERABLE TO NAILS
  ② 32:FLAT-HEAD WOOD
     SCREWS REQUIRED-
     2¼" LONG
  ③ DRILL LEAD HOLES &
     COUNTERSINK

WHITTLESEY

35

EXERCISE BENCH

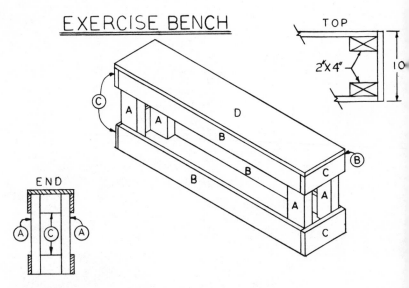

LIST OF MATERIALS:
- Ⓐ 4: 2"×4"'s-24" LONG
- Ⓑ 4: ¾"×4"-46½ LONG
- Ⓒ 4: ¾"×4"-10" LONG
- Ⓓ 1: 1" THICK PLYWOOD:
    10"×48"

36

11

Safety Factor
In Weight Training

Weight training or weight lifting is one of the safer sports. The ratio of injury is relatively low. In 1949-1950,* a study was made of 31,702 weight trainers, weight lifters and body builders, with a total of 494 accidents or 1.5 per cent. The great majority of the accidents involved muscle strains to the back, wrists and shoulders in that order. There were only five cases of hernia. Most of the muscle strains in lifting can be prevented by adhering to a few simple rules as set out below.

MEDICAL EXAMINATION — Weight training like any other physical activity imposes stresses on the human body. A prospective football player should not engage in weight training or any other type of strenuous activity without first undergoing a medical examination. The examining doctor should be made aware of any previous injury to the bone or muscle structure of the body. The athlete should not withhold any information of this type from the doctor at the time of the examination.

WARM UP — An athlete should always warm up for six to eight minutes before he begins a weight training session. A warm up including some stretching movement increases the

*Murray, Jim and Karpovich, Peter V., *Weight Training In Athletics*, Englewood Cliffs, New Jersey, Prentice-Hall, Inc., 1956.

muscle tissue elasticity, stretches the ligaments and aids in reducing stiffness. The warm up should consist of movements that are rapid and relaxed, involve little or no resistance, and imitate as closely as possible the movements to be used in the weight training session.

LIFTING FORM — Carefully read instructions on the correct way to perform the exercises. Master complicated exercises with a light weight before attempting to perform them with a heavy weight. Forcefully control all movements done with weights. Be sure the hand positions on the bar are properly spaced or the load will be unbalanced. Do not lift the weight with slippery hands — use chalk to counteract perspiration on the hands. Lift the weights in a smooth manner at a moderate pace when doing pure strength development exercises. When using speed on explosive movements, a one-half to one second contraction pause between each repetition assists in maintaining control of the weight and positioning the body with adequate balance for the next repetition. In lifting heavy weights from the floor, keep the bar close to the body with each lift, insure the back is straight with head up. Bend only with the legs and hips and keep the feet flat on the floor, shoulder width apart.

BREATHING — Generally inhale with the effort of lifting and exhale while returning the weight to the original starting position. In repetitive explosive type movements with weights involving speed of movement, it is difficult to regulate the breathing. Do not worry about regular breathing; just remember not to hold the breath for a prolonged period of time.

PARTNERS AND SPOTTERS — Most books on weight training for the athlete recomend having spotters available when the athlete is lifting heavy weights in the bench press and squat (a spotter is a person who will standby to give assistance if needed). It is fine to have a partner during training sessions, but it is not necessary in order to handle heavy weights in the squat and bench press. Here are a couple of tricks the old timers used in lifting massive weights while working out alone. If stranded in the low position of the squat and unable to rise, remove one hand from the bar, place the same hand on the thigh and press down on the thigh with the hand as you rise. The heavy weight will not come off the shoulders. In the bench press, hook the feet under the bench and simply roll the weight forward over the chest and stomach till it reaches the lower abdomen and then sit up. This is also a good way to start a bench press if stands are lacking or a partner is not available to hand you the weight. Sit down with the weight on the lap. As the upper body is lowered to the bench, roll the weight across the stomach to the pressing position at the chest.

EQUIPMENT AND EXERCISE AREA — Avoid the use of weak benches, seats that teeter or boxes that are too flimsy for the support of weights or the body. When lifting, insure that the plates and collars on the bar are securely fastened. If possible, do all weight training on a concrete or wooden floor that is not slippery. If exercising in the backyard, do so on a dirt surface or on the grass which is closely cut. The workout area should not be cluttered with loose pieces of equipment which the lifter might trip over while lifting.

CLOTHING — Wear warm clothing during the weight training session unless the exercising area is heated or during an unusually warm day. High topped tennis shoes provide good traction and ankle support.

CONDUCT — Avoid horseplay and fun type lifting. Concentrate on correct performance of the exercise and avoid any conversation during lifting. Do not engage in competitive lifting contests with a work out partner or other persons visiting the training session.

12

Weight Training Systems

All systems of weight training are based on the principle of *progressive resistance* related to the specific objective of the program whether it be strength, muscular development or muscular endurance. The factors of load (weight), repetitions, and sets are of primary importance. These factors determine whether a system is designed as single or double progressive, set, super-set, multi-poundage, etc.

LOADS AND REPETITIONS — Strength development requires the use of maximum or near maximum weights combined with low repetitions (2 to 6); strength combined with muscular development — the same weight range but using 6 to 10 repetitions; strength combined with muscular development and some degree of muscular endurance — moderate to near maximum weights with repetitions in the range from 10 to 15; muscular endurance development only — light to moderate weights employing a great number of repetitions (15 to 40); explosive power development — light to moderate weights with a moderate number of repetitions (10 to 20).

Two basic systems of weight training programs are depicted in this book. They are designed as:

1. *Double Progressive* — Used by beginning weight trainers, having no previous experience in performing the exercises listed in the basic strength conditioning course. Begin with the recommended number of repetitions for the exer-

cise. Each workout increase one repetition for arm and shoulder exercises and two repetitions for back, leg and abdomen exercises until the specified maximum number of repetitions is attained. At this point add weight and start over with the minimum repetitions. This system is also used with the football weight training program.

2. *Set System* — Also known as a single progressive system. To be used by the athlete with previous weight training experience in performing the basic strength conditioning course, and by *all* athletes in performing the injury prevention, strength development for special skills and ligament strengthening programs. A designated number of repetitions is established for a specific exercise. This is known as a set. Perform one set of repetitions per exercise for the first six to eight workouts, then add a second set, and where recommended, a third set after performing the second set for six to eight workouts. After performing three sets for six to eight workouts and being able to complete all repetitions of the three sets without too much strain, add weight to the bar but *continue with the same number of sets and repetitions.* On some occasions when weight is added, the athlete may find he cannot complete the third set of repetitions. No additional weight should be added to the bar until he has completed the required number of repetitions for all sets.

In respect to weight training systems, football coaches have adopted various approaches to the development of strength in conditioning their athletes. One of these approaches uses Isometric exercises as a sole source of strength development. An Isometric movement is the application of muscular force against an immovable object. It has been highly popularized during the past few years as a quick method of developing strength without spending much time or effort. People who have pushed this form of exercise do not tell the public or the athlete the real truth about its contribution to strength development or its limitations. Isometrics will develop a certain level of strength. True, but to what level? As one wag has stated, "Anything will work on the untrained man."

41

No evidence has been developed by modern day physiological research that Isometric training alone has ever developed a truly strong man. The weight lifting world itself has never produced an outstanding strong weightlifter through the sole use of Isometric training. The leading researchers in the physical education field maintain the most effective use of Isometrics is in the field of injury rehabilitation and strength testing.

Reliance on Isometrics alone can result in a form of *muscle boundness,* and a proness towards muscular and joint injuries. The experience of a prominent professional football team proves this point. During a summer pre-conditioning program they relied solely on the use of Isometrics for the development of strength. That fall, the team suffered more muscular and joint injuries than in any prior season. The loss of several players through injury relegated them to a very low position in league standings. The sole use of Isometrics for the development of strength in athletes whose sport involves speed of movement or muscular endurance is not justified. In this respect a basic truism of training is that you must *practice as you would perform.* Isometrics contributes little to the specific training required by any sport, with the possible exception of some static positions in gymnastics, and tends to establish patterns and physiological responses which actually interfere with successful execution of sports activities. Weight training movements have more in common with sports movements because they involve motor learning and are psychologically satisfying.

13

Weight Training Procedures

The procedures set out here are drawn from the practical world of weight lifting and body building based on century old experimentation by thousands of iron game devotees.

NUMBER OF WORKOUTS EACH WEEK — Accepted practice for beginners is three times per week with a day of rest between each workout which provides an opportunity for the muscles to grow. With a properly designed program, other activities that are done in conjunction with athletic weight training programs do not interfere with the development of strength.

LENGTH OF WORKOUT PERIOD — The average total lifting accomplished in a one hour workout is four to eight minutes. Any of the programs depicted by the writer can be completed in a total time period of one hour.

TIME OF DAY — The afternoon or evening is generally the best time to workout. If done during the evening hours it should not be sooner than one and one-half hour after dinner and completed at least one hour before going to bed.

SELECTION OF EXERCISES — Exercises should be selected to meet the objectives of the program. The approach used by the writer is based on the concept that football is a sport requiring total body effort. Therefore, we concentrate on general body exercises with the emphasis placed on the development of strength in the large muscles used in carrying out the basic skills of football — running, blocking, and tackling.

ses for injury prevention, special skills, muscle agility,
... are termed as supplementary exercises.

EXERCISE CADENCE — Strength development exercises for injury prevention, muscular or ligament strengthening should
be done at a moderate pace in a strict manner with complete
flexion and extension of the muscles directly involved. Explosive power and agility movements should be done at as fast a
pace as possible, using a definite rhythm, consistent with the
amount of weight used and the *form requirements of the
exercise.*

REST PAUSE — In performing the basic strength development exercises, a three minute rest period should be used between exercises or individual sets of an exercise, except where
highly localized muscles (neck, wrist, fingers, etc.) are being
exercised. In these localized exercises the rest period can be
reduced. The writer recommends specific rest period lengths
for the football weight training program, with the rest period
being shortened to develop aspects of cardio-pulmonary efficiency, and the psychological and physiological tolerance of
fatigue.

STARTING WEIGHT — In determining the initial starting
weight for an exercise, trial and error is still the best method.
There must be an all-out effort against resistance in order to
develop strength. When an exercise calls for a specific number
of repetitions and the weight the lifter is using does not force
a strain during the final two or three repetitions, he is not
using enough weight. Then the weight should be increased.

INCREASING WEIGHT — Add weight to the bar when you can
complete the required number of repetitions without strain
for three successive workouts. Common practice is to add 2½
to 5 pounds for arm and shoulder exercises and 5 to 10 pounds
for leg and back exercises.

MAXIMUM LOAD — The amount of weight that can be lifted
for one repetition of a specific movement. Near maximum
weights would be 85 to 98 per cent of maximum; moderate
weights 30 to 60 per cent of maximum; light weights 5 to 30
per cent of maximum.

14

The Athlete And His Muscles

Many young athletes who take up weight training, tend to overemphasize large muscular development and body size. Quality of muscular strength and proportion is far more important than quantity. Strength and a balanced muscular development are the qualities the athlete will acquire through weight training. Strength is one of the two basic factors in the development of explosive power; the other is speed. Balanced muscular development increases body coordination and flexibility, and aids in the prevention of joint injuries and muscular strains.

There are wide physical differences among young men of the same age due to inherited stature, length and thickness of bones, and the proportionate length of arms, legs and trunk. These inherent body characteristics limit the amount of strength, muscular development or body size that can be developed by an individual. The important point for the athlete to remember is that strength and muscular size can be increased through weight training and diet to the limits of inherited body structure.

Exercises in an athletic weight training routine are designed to increase strength in those muscles involved in the movement patterns used by the athlete in his sport. For this reason every football player should know the terminology used in describing muscle action.

A muscle can only do two things; contract or relax. When muscle contracts it is called an agonist (mover) which is the name for the joint action that results from the contraction. A prime mover is a muscle that is primarily responsible for bringing about a specified joint action. An antagonist is a muscle whose contraction will produce a joint action exactly opposite to the joint action caused by a specific prime mover muscle. A stabilizer muscle is one which anchors or supports a bone or body part so another active (prime) muscle will have a firm base on which to pull. A neutralizer muscle is one that contracts to counteract or neutralize an undesired action of another contracting muscle.

A muscle seldom, if ever, acts alone. Most muscles have more than one joint action. When they contract they require the contraction of other muscles as neutralizers and other muscles as stabilizers.

Coaches and trainers in establishing weight training routines for a specific sport place the emphasis on development of strength in the prime mover muscles involved in the movement pattern of the sport. Strength development at a comparable level for the antagonistic muscles should not be overlooked. Overdevelopment of one muscle at the expense of its antagonist can lead to *muscle boundness* with restricted joint action and/or loss of speed. Overdevelopment of muscles on one side of the body joint and neglect of the antagonistic muscles place the antagonist under constant stress. This leads to premature fatigue in the antagonistic muscle and makes the joint much more susceptible to injury. The constant stress on the underdeveloped antagonistic muscles and the lack of flexibility in the overdeveloped prime movers make it extremely difficult to relax the antagonistic muscles when the prime movers go into action. The secret of the champion athlete's well coordinated, fast, explosive movement is directly related to his ability to exert a maximum contraction of the prime mover muscles while completely relaxing the antagonistic muscles.

Muscles are also classified by the action of a body joint or part that results from the contraction of the muscle. Two of the classifications which should be familiar to athletes are flexors (a bending or flexing muscle) and extensors (a straightening or extending muscle). In explaining exercises and their effect upon certain muscles the anatomical names are used. The accompanying chart will be of assistance in identifying their location in relation to the body structure.

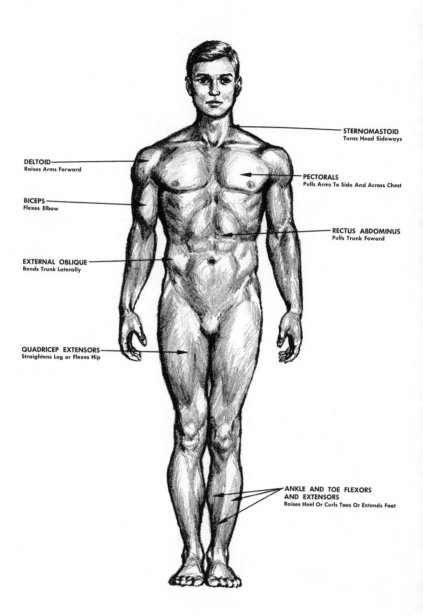

STERNOMASTOID
Turns Head Sideways

DELTOID
Raises Arms Forward

PECTORALS
Pulls Arms To Side And Across Chest

BICEPS
Flexes Elbow

RECTUS ABDOMINUS
Pulls Trunk Foward

EXTERNAL OBLIQUE
Bends Trunk Laterally

QUADRICEP EXTENSORS
Straightens Leg or Flexes Hip

**ANKLE AND TOE FLEXORS
AND EXTENSORS**
Raises Heel Or Curls Toes Or Extends Foot

48

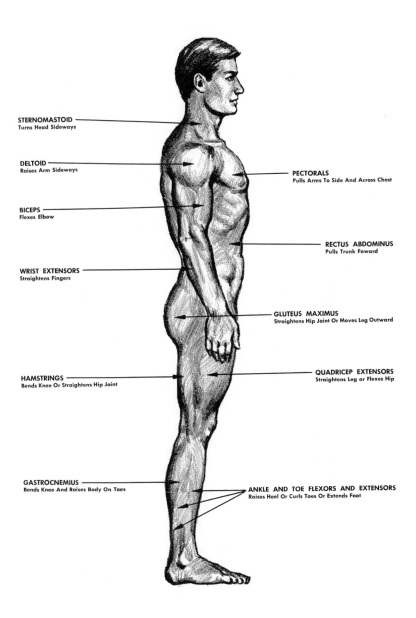

STERNOMASTOID
Turns Head Sideways

DELTOID
Raises Arm Sideways

BICEPS
Flexes Elbow

WRIST EXTENSORS
Straightens Fingers

HAMSTRINGS
Bends Knee Or Straightens Hip Joint

GASTROCNEMIUS
Bends Knee And Raises Body On Toes

PECTORALS
Pulls Arms To Side And Across Chest

RECTUS ABDOMINUS
Pulls Trunk Foward

GLUTEUS MAXIMUS
Straightens Hip Joint Or Moves Leg Outward

QUADRICEP EXTENSORS
Straightens Leg or Flexes Hip

ANKLE AND TOE FLEXORS AND EXTENSORS
Raises Heel Or Curls Toes Or Extends Foot

49

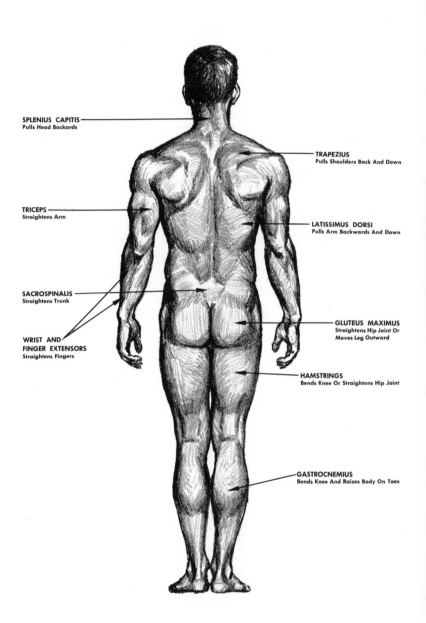

SPLENIUS CAPITIS
Pulls Head Backards

TRAPEZIUS
Pulls Shoulders Back And Down

TRICEPS
Straightens Arm

LATISSIMUS DORSI
Pulls Arm Backwards And Down

SACROSPINALIS
Straightens Trunk

GLUTEUS MAXIMUS
Straightens Hip Joint Or
Moves Leg Outward

WRIST AND
FINGER EXTENSORS
Straightens Fingers

HAMSTRINGS
Bends Knee Or Straightens Hip Joint

GASTROCNEMIUS
Bends Knee And Raises Body On Toes

15

Program Schedules

An off-season weight training program should cover a period of approximately seven months. The first session should begin in December and terminate at the start of spring practice and the second session should begin at the close of spring practice and terminate at the start of the fall football season.

The following suggestions concerning participation in the off-season weight training program are offered:

1. A young high school athlete with no previous weight training experience should spend approximately six months on the basic strength conditioning program. The athlete should use the double progressive system of weights and repetitions, then supplement the basic course with the injury prevention program (except the ligament strengthening exercises) and the flexibility program. This covers the period from the first of December until spring practice, and from the close of spring practice until the first of July. The athlete then begins the football weight training program in place of the basic course and continues with the injury prevention and flexibility programs. He should also include the ligament strengthening exercises which could be performed on the non-weight training days.

2. A high school athlete with previous weight training experience should spend six weeks on the basic strength con-

ditioning program using the set system of weights and repetitions, supplemented by the injury prevention program (with exception of ligament strengthening exercises) and the flexibility exercise program. This covers the period from the first of December to the latter part of January. At this point he begins the football weight training program three days per week and continues with the injury prevention program (except ligament strengthening exercises) and the flexibility exercises until the start of spring practice. At the conclusion of spring practice he resumes the football weight training, the injury prevention and the flexibility programs. About July 1st, he should start the ligament strengthening exercises, and these may be done on the days while not weight training. The athlete should continue the football, injury prevention and flexibility programs until the start of the fall season practice.

3. The above schedules do not apply to the athlete engaged in the specific weight gaining program set out in this book. Any athlete performing the basic or football weight training program will gain muscular weight if he increases his food intake. There are some cases where an athlete has great difficulty in gaining weight. This program will give him the desired results if he will adhere to the directions accompanying the program. We mentioned previously that the athlete under 16 years of age should not engage in this program without having at least six months training on the basic strength conditioning course.

4. The athlete interested in losing weight can perform the basic and football programs and at the same time reduce his food intake. The writer does not believe in the concept of using weight training with increased repetitions for the specific purpose of losing weight. The overweight athlete still requires strength, power and agility. He can loose weight much quicker by engaging in other forms of activity, the best of these being running. These other activities should be done after the weight training session or on the alternate days.

5. All athletes intending to participate in football should actively engage in other forms of athletics on the non-weight

training days. Basketball, volleyball, handball, speedball, soccer, etc., are sports which promote general body coordination, lateral rotational mobility, quickness, ability to react and body balance in addition to muscular and cardio-respiratory endurance. Above all the athlete should engage in running, particularly short sprints and sidewards and backwards running. His goal should be to develop the kind of endurance that enables him to run 15 to 35 yards at top speed in all directions continuously for a period from 15 to 20 minutes with rest periods not exceeding 15 seconds. Potential ends, flanker backs and runners should extend the straight ahead sprints to 50 yards, and reduce their complete rest intervals to 10 seconds. If they run 50 yards they should follow it with a slow jog of 30 yards and a slow walk of 15 yards before repeating their run.

A word about this type of running. It is well to begin with five minutes total running time early in the off-season and gradually increase from 15 to 20 minutes. Early in the off-season the rest intervals may be as long as 30 seconds but should be gradually reduced to 15 seconds.

7. Here are a few tips for in-season training. Studies have shown that arm, shoulder and neck strength of football players decreases during the competitive season as blocking and tackling in themselves do not provide enough resistance to maintain the degree of strength previously developed in these areas of the body. The following exercises should be done the first three days of the week during the season after completion of regular practice: (A) Buddy type neck exercises; (B) Wheelbarrow walk and dips on hands; (C) Chinning.

16

Warm Up

This schedule or a similar one should be performed prior to the basic strength conditioning or football weight training programs.

Sprinter

STARTING POSITION: Squat, hands on the floor, right leg fully extended to rear. ACTION: Reverse position of feet in bouncing movement, bringing right foot to hands and extending left leg backward, all in one motion. REPETITIONS: 20.

Sitting Stretch

STARTING POSITION: Sit on the floor with legs spread, fingers locked behind neck. ACTION: Bend forward, reaching elbows as close to the floor as possible. Return to starting position. REPITITIONS: 20.

Push Ups

STARTING POSITION: Lie on the floor, face down, hands on the floor under shoulders, fingers pointing straight ahead and elbows back. ACTION: Push the body off the floor by extending arms so weight rests on hands and toes. Body should be kept straight, abdomen not sagging. REPETITIONS: 12.

Running In Place

ACTION: Raise each foot at least four inches off the floor and jog in place for 20 seconds. During the next ten seconds, raise legs high and pump arms vigorously. Return to jogging for 20 seconds and repeat ten second vigorous run four times for a total of two minutes running in place.

17

Basic Football
Weight Training Program

PROGRAM FUNDAMENTALS — (A) The double progressive system of weight and repetition increase is used except for exercises No. 4 and No. 6, where repetitions only are increased; (B) Increase one repetition each workout. When maximum repetitions are reached, continue for four workouts at the same repetitions. Then increase weights and start over at minimum repetitions; (C) All exercises except No. 6 are classed as explosive movements and should be done at as fast a pace as possible, consistent with the weight used and the form requirements of the exercise; (D) Every effort should be made to gradually reduce the suggested rest intervals to a period of 60 to 90 seconds maximum; (E) In the movements requiring alternate rotation of the body or movement of the legs, forward and backward as in exercise No. 2, the total reps would be double the amount listed; (F) Start with light or moderate weights, but add weight regularly; (G) Where a chinning bar (exercise No. 6) or workout partner is not available (exercise No. 5), do the alternate exercises listed.

EXERCISE	REPETITIONS	REST INTERVAL	WEIGHT INCREASE
1. Continuous Clean & Press	10 through 15	1 Min	5 lbs
2. Bouncing Split Squat	8 through 12	3 Min.	2½ lbs
3. Continuous Pull to Chin	10 through 15	3 Min.	5 lbs.

4. Wheelbarrow Walk & Dips	Walk 10 yards and 5 dips	2 Min.	Increase 10 yards every week, until 50 yards is reached. Each 10 yards do 5 dips.
5. Bend Over Twist	8 through 12	1 Min.	2½ lbs.
6. Overhand Chins	2 sets — 5 re-petitions	1 Min.	Increase 1 rep. each set every week.
7. Jumping Squats	15 through 20	3 Min.	2½ lbs.
8. Twisting Sit-Ups	8 through 12	1 Min	2½ lbs.
9. Barbell Swing	8 through 12		2½ lbs.

ALTERNATE EXERCISES

EXERCISE	REPETITIONS	REST INTERVAL	WEIGHT INCREASE
A. Bench Press	6	3 Min.	5 lbs. every 2 weeks
B. Wrist Curls	10	3 Min.	2½ lbs. every 2 weeks
C. Bent Over Rowing Motion	6	3 Min.	5 lbs. every 2 weeks

Continuous Clean & Press

STARTING POSITION: Weight on floor, hands shoulder width apart, feet 16 to 18 inches apart, back straight and head up. ACTION: Raise weight to shoulders and without stopping press overhead to full arms extension. Lower to shoulders and then to floor. Repeat immediately.

Bouncing Split Squat

STARTING POSITION: Stand erect, weight on shoulders. ACTION: Leap into air, at same time splitting legs forwards and backwards as shown. When landing, get hips as low as possible. *Immediately rebound* as high as possible reversing direction of legs. No hesitation between jumps, but a continuous movement. NOTE: Extremely effective for development of explosive power in legs and increasing flexibility in the hips.

Continuous Pull To Chin

STARTING POSITION: Weight on floor, hands 6 inches apart, feet 16 to 18 inches apart, head up and back straight. ACTION: Pull weight to chin level, keeping elbows up as weight reaches above waist level. Raise on toes as weight reaches chest level. Let weight drop to straight arm hang position at hips. Then lower weight to about 3 inches from floor and repeat pull. On remaining repetitions do not let weight touch floor. Hesitate for 1 second before starting next pull.

Wheelbarrow Walk & Dips

STARTING POSITION: Legs held high under partner's arms. ACTION: Walk 10 yards on hands, then perform 5 dips—touching chin to ground. After each 10 yards perform 5 dips.

Bend Over Twist

STARTING POSITION: Stand erect, weight on shoulders, hands just inside collars of barbell, feet 20 to 24 inches apart. ACTION: Bend forward, dipping right shoulder and attempting to touch left toe with barbell handle. Come erect and repeat to opposite foot. Do not use hurried motions.

Overhand Chins

STARTING POSITION: Hang at arms level, hands shoulder width apart. ACTION: Pull slowly up, until chin is above bar. Lower and repeat.

Jumping Squats

STARTING POSITION: Stand erect, barbell on shoulders, feet 16 to 18 inches apart. ACTION: Leap high into air as possible. Drop into squat position, thighs slightly lower than parallel to ground. Immediately rebound and leap into air without stopping.

Twisting Sit Ups

STARTING POSITION: Lie on floor, weight held behind neck, feet tied or held down, about 12 to 14 inches apart, knees slightly bent. ACTION: Curl trunk forward with chin on chest. As you come erect make violent effort to touch right elbow to left knee. Lower and repeat to opposite side.

Barbell Swing

STARTING POSITION: Stand erect, weight held in hands at hip level, slightly wider than shoulder level. ACTION: Raise weight to overhead position, twisting trunk and hips to right while doing so. Lower and repeat to opposite side.

ALTERNATE EXERCISES

Bench Press

STARTING POSITION: Lie on bench, holding weight on chest, with hands slightly wider than shoulder width. ACTION: Push weight away from chest until arms are completely straight. Lower to chest and repeat.

Wrist Curls

STARTING POSITION: Sitting on edge of chair or kneeling at bench as depicted, support forearms on thighs or on bench. Grasp barbell with palms upward. ACTION: Raise and lower weight by flexing and extending wrists. As hand is lowered, bar should be permitted to roll down to finger tips. The exercise should also be done with palms down for the wrist extensors.

Bent Over Rowing Motion

STARTING POSITION: Legs slightly bent, lean forward with trunk in a nearly horizontal position, back straight, head up, grasping bar with over-grip, hands slightly narrower than shoulder width apart. ACTION: Without any motion of the body or legs, pull weight up until bar touches body near middle of the abdomen. Keep elbows close to sides when raising weight. Lower weight to within 6 inches of floor and repeat.

18

Injury Prevention Program

PROGRAM FUNDAMENTALS — (A) Suggested weight increase added when the athlete can perform all sets and repetitions without strain for three consecutive workouts; (B) A barbell handle and two iron boots will make a perfect substitute as a leg extension and leg curl machine; (C) On the buddy type exercises, steady pressure should be used by the partner applying the resistance.

EXERCISE	SETS	REPETITIONS	WEIGHT INCREASE
1. Leg Extension	3	10	5 lbs.
2. Leg Curl	3	10	5 lbs.
3. Neck Strap or Buddy Type Neck Exercises	3	10	5 lbs.
4. Bar Hang Drop	3	5	Increase Repetitions

Leg Extension

STARTING POSITION: Seated on bench, legs bent at knees. ACTION: Slowly raise lower legs to horizontal position, holding weight with knees locked at the horizontal position for a count of two, then lower weight.

Leg Curl

STARTING POSITION: Lie on bench, face down, legs extended. ACTION: Raise heels towards buttocks—then lower.

NOTE: There is a strong tendency by athletes to emphasize development of the quadriceps (front of thigh) and neglect development of the hamstrings (rear of thigh). A balanced development is absolutely essential to protection of the knee joint. Studies have shown the hamstrings should have 60 percent as much strength as that possesed by the quadriceps. For example, if 80 lbs. is used in the leg extension exercie, 50 lbs. should be used in the leg curl to insure a balanced increase of strength in both groups of muscles.

Neck Strap Exercise

STARTING POSITION: Kneel on bench, head must be lower than shoulders. ACTION: Raise head slowly upward as far as possible without hands leaving bench.

Neck Strap Exercise

STARTING POSITION: Be seated on a bench in a lean-back position, with head in a downwards position. ACTION: Raise head upwards and forwards until chin touches the chest without hands leaving the bench.

Buddy Type Neck Exercise

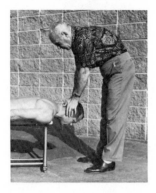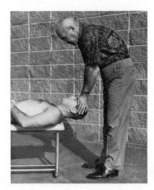

STARTING POSITION: Lie face down on bench, head extended over the end of the bench. ACTION: Partner places hands on back of head and applies pressure while the athlete resists. Head is pushed down as far as possible. Raise head against resistance. Reverse position and lay down on the bench face up. Partner now applies pressure to forehead. Raise head against resistance.

Bar Hang Drop

STARTING POSITION: Hang by the arms on overhead bar. ACTION: Pull the body up about six inches. Relax muscles of the arms completely and then drop to full arm hanging position.

19

Strength Development For Special Skills

PROGRAM FUNDAMENTALS — (A) On exercise No. 4 the Shoulder Push, the starting weight should be 30 to 40 pounds more than the best bench press poundage; (B) Suggested increase should be added when all sets and repetitions are completed without strain for three consecutive workouts.

PASSERS — Exercises Nos. 1 through 4. KICKERS — Exercise No. 5.

EXERCISE	REPETITIONS	SETS	WEIGHT INCREASE
1. Tricep Extension	10	3	2½ lbs.
2. Wrist Extension (Front)	10	3	1¼ lbs.
3. Wrist Extension (Back)	10	3	1¼ lbs.
4. Shoulder Push	15	3	20 lbs.
5. Standing Straight Leg Raise	10	3	2½ lbs.

Tricep Extension

STARTING POSITION: Hold barbell above head, hands 12 inches apart; palms facing to the front. ACTION: Slowly lower weight to back of neck, maintaining elbows in an *upright position at all times*. Return to starting position.

Wrist Extension

STARTING POSITION: Hold dumbell handle with weighted end in a downward position alongside the thigh. ACTION: Raise weight to a horizontal position to front of body. Reverse starting position and raise weighted end to the rear.

Shoulder Push

STARTING POSITION: Lie on bench, weight overhead, hands shoulder width apart. ACTION: Raise weight upward with shoulder movement only (about 3 to 4 inches) maintaining straight arms, locked at elbows.

Standing Straight Leg Raise

STARTING POSITION: Standing on bench, supporting body balance with hand opposite to leg being raised. ACTION: Raise leg to height of hips. Use moderate pace in raising and lowering leg.

20

Ligament
Strengthening Program

PROGRAM FUNDAMENTALS — (A) Exercises for knee joints should not be performed until the athlete can perform a leg extension (both legs) with 120 pounds for 10 repetitions, and a leg curl (both legs) with 75 pounds for 10 repetitions; (B) Added resistance can be applied by a workout partner pressing on the joint involved.

EXERCISE	SETS AND REPETITIONS
1. Ankle Ligaments*	Repeat routine 3 times
2. Outer Knee Ligaments*	Repeat routine 3 times
3. Inner Knee Ligaments*	Repeat routine 3 times
4. Shoulder Ligaments	2 sets — 10 repetitions

Ankle Ligaments Exercise

STARTING POSITION: Front leaning rest, feet extended, resting on back (top) of feet. ACTION: (A) Bounce up and down on toes three times; (B) Turn trunk to left, supporting feet on lower side of ankle. Bounce three times; (C) Same to the right; (D) Turn back to front, leaning rest, supporting feet on inner borders, and bounce up and down three times.

Outer Knee Ligaments Exercise

STARTING POSITION: Side leaning rest on left hand and left foot, right foot resting on inner side of left knee. ACTION: (A) Raise outer side of left ankle from floor and bounce up and down three times; (B) Counterlike same action.

Inner Knee Ligaments Exercise

STARTING POSITION: Side leaning rest on left hand and right foot, left foot (outer side of ankle) resting atop right knee. ACTION: (A) Raise outer side of right ankle. Bounce up and down three times. (B) Counterlike same action.

Shoulder Ligaments Exercise

STARTING POSITION: Hang by arms on overhead bar. ACTION: Pull body up about six inches. Relax muscles of the arms completely and then drop full to arm hanging position.

*Exercises Nos. 1, 2 and 3 reproduced with permission from the brochure *DO IT YOURSELF — PREVENT INJURY* published by the National Federation of State High School Association and developed by Dr. C. H. McCloy, University of Iowa.

21

Flexibility Program

The *Basic* and *Football Strength* programs incorporate exercises that promote lower back flexibility and while the *Injury Prevention* program includes an exercise that develops shoulder flexibility an additional program is required. This abbreviated program outlines exercises for the development of flexibility in the "hamstring" and the groin (hip flexors). Either of the hamstring exercises should be performed immediately following the leg curl movement presented in the Injury Prevention program. The leg curl is essential for the development of strength in the muscles supporting the knee joint but tends to shorten the hamstrings. All players should perform the groin area flexibility exercise every day. Hip flexibility permits the athlete to attain a low, well balanced position in applying the basic skills of blocking and tackling.

EXERCISES	SETS	REPETITIONS	BODY AREA AFFECTED
1. Seated Toe Touch	3	10 to 15 bounces	Hamstrings
2. Fore & Aft Split	3	5 to 10 bounces	Hamstrings
3. Prone Body Dip	3	10 to 15 bounces	Groin

74

Seated Toe Touch

STARTING POSITION: Seated with legs together. ACTION: Reach forward and extend hands toward toes while bent forward. Release hands from toes approximately three or four inches, then recontact toes. REPETITIONS: 10 to 15 times.

Fore & Aft Split

STARTING POSITION: Split position with right leg forward, supporting body with both hands on the ground. ACTION: Bounce gently up and down 5 to 10 times. Perform also with left leg forward.

75

Prone Body Dip

STARTING POSITION: As shown in the photograph. ACTION: Bounce groin up and down two to three inches as the head is moved forward and backward the same distance, 10 to 15 times.

22

Basic Strength Conditioning Program

PROGRAM FUNDAMENTALS — (A) Increase one repetition each workout; (B) Suggested weight increases are made when maximum repetitions are reached; (C) With weight increase start over at minimum repetitions; (D) Movements should be done at a moderate pace with complete flexion and extension of the muscles involved.

EXERCISES	REPETITIONS	WEIGHT INCREASE
1. Clean and Press	7 through 12	5 lbs
2. Upright Rowing Motion	7 through 12	5 lbs
3. Squat	15 through 20	10 lbs
4. Bench Press	7 through 12	5 lbs
5. Bent Over Rowing Motion	7 through 12	5 lbs
6. Side Bend	7 through 12 (each side)	5 lbs
7. Raise on Toes	15 through 20	10 lbs
8. Straight Legged Dead Lift	7 through 12	5 lbs
9. Twisting Sit-Up	7 through 12 (each side)	5 lbs
10. Power Curl	7 through 12	5 lbs

Clean and Press

STARTING POSITION: Bend forward, grasp weight with hands slightly wider than shoulder width. Head up and back straight. ACTION: Pull weight to shoulders. Hesitate for count of one, then press overhead to arms length. Return to shoulder level and repeat.

Upright Rowing Motion

STARTING POSITION: Stand erect grasping barbell held at arms length in front of body at hip level. Place hands six inches apart with palms facing body. ACTION: Raise weight to chin level with elbows always staying higher than the weight. Return to starting position.

Squat

STARTING POSITION: Stand erect with barbell on the shoulders, feet spaced 16 to 18 inches apart, with toes pointed slightly outwards. ACTION: Lower body to where thighs are parallel to the ground. Without hesitation, rise to an erect position. Breathe in as you lower weight, with head erect and back straight. Exhale as you rise to erect position. NOTE: A two by four piece of wood under the heels will assist in maintaining balance.

Bench Press

STARTING POSITION: Lie on bench. Hold weight on chest with hands slightly wider than shoulder width. ACTION: Push weight away from chest until arms are completely straight. Lower to chest and repeat.

Bent Over Rowing Motion

STARTING POSITION: Legs slightly bent, lean forward with trunk in a nearly horizontal position, back straight, head up, grasping bar with overgrip. Hands slightly narrower than shoulder width apart. ACTION: Without any motion of the body or legs, pull weight up until bar touches near the middle of the adbomen. Keep elbows close to sides when raising weight. Lower weight to within six inches of floor and repeat.

Side Bend

STARTING POSITION: Stand erect with weight held on shoulders. Grasp bar just inside collars with feet 16 inches apart. ACTION: Bend to right as far as possible. Return to erect position and bend to the other side.

Raise On Toes

STARTING POSITION: Stand erect with barbell held behind neck on shoulders. Place toes on a two by four block of wood with feet about 12 inches apart. ACTION: Raise body by elevating heels and rising onto balls of feet. Return to starting position. NOTE: Do one set with toes pointed outward, one set with toes pointed inward.

Straight Legged Dead Lift

STARTING POSITION: Stand erect holding barbell at arms length in front of body with palms facing body. Hands should be shoulder width apart. ACTION: Bend forward and lower bar as far as possible, keeping arms straight and knees locked.

81

Twisting Sit Up

STARTING POSITION: Lie on floor with weight behind the neck. Feet should be tied or held down and placed about 12 to 14 inches apart. Knees must be slightly bent as in the illustration. ACTION: Curl trunk forward with chin on chest. As you come erect, make a violent effort to touch the right elbow to the left knee. Lower and repeat to the opposite side.

Power Curl

STARTING POSITION: Bend down and grasp the barbell with undergrip. Hands should be placed shoulder width apart. ACTION: Curl the bar to the shoulder level and rise to an erect standing position in one continuous movement. Return to the starting position and repeat.

23

Weight Gaining Program

This program is designed for the athlete who has great difficulty in gaining muscular body weight with traditional weight training programs.

The backbone of the program is the use of heavy squats in conjunction with a weight gaining diet, plenty of sleep, and *no other type of physical activity* during the period in which the program is being used. This approach to weight gaining in the body building field was first introduced in America by Mark Berry during the 1930's. Fantastic gains in muscular bulk were realized in a few months by men who had tried for years to gain weight with the established body building methods of that era. If the athlete strictly adheres to the directions given and is willing to work hard, the writer almost guarantees the athlete can add 15 to 20 pounds of muscular weight in 8 to 10 weeks.

LENGTH OF PROGRAM — Total period — 10 weeks. The first two weeks should be the "breaking in" period when the athlete conditions his body to the added work and increased food intake. The best time to participate in this program is during the months of December through February.

SLEEP — Nine to ten hours *every* night.

83

MENTAL ATTITUDE — The athlete must learn to physically relax outside of workout periods, but to work hard when exercising. This is a strenuous program and maximum weights should be used.

DIET — Increase food intake to 5,500 calories per day. Increase protein intake to 150 grams per day. Most athletes will experience difficulty in handling this amount of food at the outset of the program. Gradually increase the amount eaten during the "breaking in" period. Eat five or six small meals rather than three large meals. The instructions given in the section on nutrition provides a guideline for a weight gaining diet.

EXERCISE PERFORMANCE — As already stated, the squat is the basic exercise for weight gaining. In using heavy weights, supports to hold the weight are required. If the bar bothers the neck, wrap a towel around the bar. The athlete should place the bar on the shoulders, then space the feet about 14 to 18 inches apart with the toes pointed slightly outward. A one and one-half to two-inch board under the heels is recommended. Breathing correctly provides over half the benefits of this exercise. With the bar on the shoulders, take three deep breaths through the mouth, lifting the chest high on each breath. Hold the third breath and lower into the squat position, thighs parallel to the ground or slightly lower. Don't remain in this position. Return to the upright position as quickly as possible. As an erect position is resumed, expel the air from the lungs through the mouth, take three more breaths and perform another squat.

Always keep the back flat and the head up. Do not allow the hips to swing up first; come erect in the same position as the body was lowered. At the finish of the required repetitions, there should be panting and heavy breathing. In most cases when the last few repetitions of a set are reached, it will be necessary to take five or six breaths between each squat. Always *hold the breath* when lowering the body into the squat position. Use as heavy a weight as possible and keep adding poundage at regular intervals. *Hard work is es-*

sential. On the second and third sets, add 20 pounds to the bar each set, but reduce the number of repetitions. Rest intervals between squat sets should be five to seven minutes including the pullover exercise.

Immediately following each set of squats, while breathing heavily, perform a set of breathing pullovers, *using the bar only.* Breathe in as the weight is lowered and make every attempt to keep the small of the back flat on the bench. Breathe out when the bar reaches the horizontal position behind the head and breathe in when returning to the overhead position. The purpose of this exercise is to stretch the rib box and make the chest grow; therefore, weight is not important.

EXERCISE	SETS	REPETITIONS	SUGGESTED WEIGHT INCREASE
1. Squat	3	15-12-8	10 lbs.—all sets
2. Breathing Pullover	2	15	Use barbell handle only—no weight increases
3. Bench Press	3	10-8-6	10 lbs.—all sets
4. Bent Over Rowing Motion	3	10-8-6	10 lbs.—all sets

Perform these exercises three times per week: Monday, Wednesday, and Friday — rest completely on the other days of the week.

Squat

STARTING POSITION: Stand erect with barbell on shoulders and feet spaced 16 to 18 inches apart. Toes pointing slightly outwards. ACTION: Lower the body to where the thighs are parallel to the ground. Without hesitation, rise to an erect position. Breathe in as you lower weight with head erect and back straight. Exhale as you rise to erect position. NOTE: A two by four piece of wood under the heels will help maintain balance.

Breathing Pullover

STARTING POSITION: Lie on the bench with face up and barbell held at a full arm extension position over chest. Hands at shoulder width and palms facing forward. ACTION: Lower bar with completely straight arms to a position behind head. Return to starting position. NOTE: Inhale as you lower weight. Try and keep small of back on bench. Exhale as the bar comes to a straight arm position over chest. Purpose of exercise is to stretch rib-box and weight should never be added to bar.

Bench Press

STARTING POSITION: Lie on bench, holding weight on chest with hands slightly wider than shoulder width. ACTION: Push weight away from chest until arms are completely straight. Lower to chest and repeat.

Bent Over Rowing Motion

STARTING POSITION: Legs slightly bent, lean forward with trunk in a nearly horizontal position, back straight, head up, grasping bar with overgrip, hands slightly narrower than shoulder width apart. ACTION: Without any motion of the body or legs, pull weight up until bar touches body near middle of the abdomen. Keep elbows close to sides when raising weight. Lower weight to within six inches of the floor and repeat.

Index

HIGH CALORIE FOODS

Number
of Calories

MEAT, POULTRY, FISH

Beef Pot Roast	2 thin slices, 4"x2½"	256
Beef Roast	2 thin slices, 4"x2½"	375
Broiled steak	2 thin slices, 4"x2½"	330
Ground hamburger	3 ounce patty (4 to pound)	245
Corned beef hash (canned)	half cup	155
Beef and vegetable stew	half cup	105
Chile Con Carne (canned)	half cup	255
Broiled veal cutlet	1 thick slice, 4"x2½"	185
Roast leg lamb	1 thick slice, 3½"x3"	235
Roast loin pork	1 thick slice, 4"x2½"	310
Ham (baked)	1 thick slice, 4"x2"	245
Bacon	2 thin slices	100
Bologna sausage	2 thin slices, 4" diameter	170
Frankfurter	one	155
Boiled ham luncheon meat	2 thin slices, 2½"x3½"	135
Broiled chicken	¼ of small broiler	185
Fried chicken	thigh and drumstick	225
Fish sticks	Five sticks	200
Broiled salmon	4½"x2½"x ½"	205
Sardines (in oil)	5 to 7 medium sardines	175
Canned tuna fish (in oil)	2/5 of cup	170

MILK AND MILK BEVERAGES

Whole	1 cup or glass	160
Half and Half (milk and cream)	1 cup	325
Cocoa (all milk)	1 cup	235
Chocolate flavored milk	1 cup	280
Malted milk	1 cup	280
Chocolate milk shake	12 ounce container	520
Chocolate ice cream soda	1 large glass	455

CHEESE

American cheddar	1¼ inch cube	115
Swiss	1¼ inch cube	105
Cream	2 tablespoons	105

NUTS

Shelled almonds	2 tablespoons	105
Roasted cashew	2 tablespoons	95
Roasted shelled peanuts	2 tablespoons	105
Peanut butter	1 tablespoon	95
Shelled walnuts chopped	2 tablespoons	100

DRY BEANS AND PEAS

Red kidney beans	½ cup	115
Cooked lima beans	½ cup	130
Baked beans with pork	½ cup	160

91

VEGETABLES

Green Lima beans	½ cup	80
Corn on Cob	1 ear, 5 inches long	70
Baked potato	1 medium, 2½" in diameter	90
French fried	10-2"x½"x½"	155
Hash browned potatoes	½ cup	225
Sweet potato	1 medium, 5"x2"	155

FRUITS

Avocado	½ of 10 ounce-3½"x 4½ inches	185
Banana	6"x1½" inches	85
Dates (pitted)	½ cup	245
Raw figs	3 small	90
Fruit Cocktail	½ cup	100
Raw pear	3"x1½"	100
Prunes, dried, cooked (sweetened)	½ cup	255
Raisins, dried	½ cup	230

BAKED GOODS

Baking powder biscuit	2½" in diameter	140
Corn muffin	2¾" in diameter	150
Cheese pizza	⅛"x14" pie	185
Roll, hard round	1 roll	160
Waffle	4½"x5½"x ½"	210

CEREALS

Puffed corn	1 cup	110
Corn flakes	1⅓ cup	110
Cooked macaroni	½ cup	235
Oatmeal or rolled oats	¾ cup	100
Cooked rice	¾ cup	140
Cooked spaghetti	¾ cup	115
Spaghetti, cheese & tomato sauce	¾ cup	195
Wheat, rolled, cooked	¾ cup	130
Wheat flakes	¾ cup	100

SOUPS

Bean with pork	1 cup	170
Cream of aspargus	1 cup	155
Cream of mushroom	1 cup	135
Minestrone	1 cup	105

DRESSINGS AND OTHER

Butter or margarine	1 pat or square	50
Vegetable cooking fat	1 tablespoon	110
Mayonnaise	1 tablespoon	110
Cheese sauce	½ cup	245

DESSERTS

Cornstarch pudding	½ cup	140
Custard, baked	½ cup	140
Ice Cream, plain	1 container (3½ ounces)	130

Fig bars	1 small	55
Apple pie	1/7 of 9 inch pie	345
Cherry pie	1/7 of 9 inch pie	355
Mince pie	1/7 of 9 inch pie	365

LOW CALORIE FOODS

		Number of Calories
MEAT, POULTRY, FISH		
Beef Pot Roast (lean only)	2 thin slices, 4"x2½"	140
Beef Roast (lean only)	2 thin slices, 4"x2"	115
Broiled steak (lean only)	2 thin slices, 4"x1½"	115
Hamburger (lean ground round)	3 ounce patty (4 to pound)	185
Dried chipped beef	½ cup	115
Lamb chop (lean only)	small chop	140
Roast loin pork (lean only)	2 thin slices, 3"x2½"	175
Cured ham (lean only)	2 thin slices, 3½"x2"	120
Beef liver	1 thick piece, 3"x2½"	130
Chicken broiled	¼ small broiler	185
Bluefish baked	1 piece, 3½"x2"x½"	135
Salmon canned	3/5 cup	120
Shrimp canned	17 medium shrimp	100
Eggs, hard or soft boiled	1 large	80
Egg poached	1 large	80
MILK		
Skim milk	1 cup or glass	90
Buttermilk	1 cup or glass	90
Cottage cheese	2 tablespoons	30
VEGETABLES		

All vegetables except fried or hash browned potatoes

FRUITS

All raw fruit except avocado, dates, raisins or canned fruits packed in syrup

BAKED GOODS		
Bread (different types)	1 slice, ½" thick	55 to 60
Crackers (saltine)	two—2" square	35
CEREALS		
Bran flakes	4/5 cup	85
Farina cooked	¾ cup	75
Rice puffed	1 cup	55
SOUPS		
Beef noodle	1 cup	70
Bouillon	1 cup	30
Chicken noodle	1 cup	65

Low calorie salad	1 tablespoon	15

DESSERTS

Fruit ice	½ cup	75
Gelatin plain	½ cup	70

SOME HIGH PROTEIN FOODS

		Number of Grams
Milk	1 quart	35 grams
Eggs	1 medium	7 grams
Cheeses, most kinds	1¼" cube	5-7 grams
Beef	per pound	Approx. 100 grams
Chicken	per pound	" 80 grams
Tuna	per pound	" 150 grams
Gelatin dried	per pound	" 400 grams
Bean (peas, navy or lima beans)	½ cup	6 grams
Soybeans	¼ cup	6 grams